Terrific practice for White Rose Maths from CGP!

This marvellous CGP workbook is matched to the White Rose Maths Scheme of Learning — great for helping pupils practise their skills.

It's jam-packed with questions for every block and small step of Year 2 Autumn Term — so you know it has everything pupils need.

Plus there are plenty of Problem Solving and Reasoning questions to check they know their stuff. Oh, and don't forget, we've included the answers to every question online — just scan the QR code at the end of the contents page. You're welcome!

What CGP is all about

Our sole aim here at CGP is to produce the highest quality books — carefully written, immaculately presented and dangerously close to being funny.

Then we work our socks off to get them out to you — at the cheapest possible prices.

Contents

Block 3 — Shape

Online Extras

The **answers** to every question in the book are available **online** — to find them, scan the QR code on the left or go to cgpbooks.co.uk/rose

Published by CGP

Editors:
Michael Bushell, Daniel Chapero-Hall, Jake McGuffie, Alison Palin, Caley Simpson, Julie Wakeling

ISBN: 978 1 83774 170 0

With thanks to Emily Forsberg and Emma Wright for the proofreading.
With thanks to Jade Sim for the copyright research.

Images on the cover and throughout the book © Educlips 2024

Printed by Elanders Ltd, Newcastle upon Tyne.
Based on the classic CGP style created by Richard Parsons.

About This Book

- This book matches the <u>White Rose Maths</u> Scheme of Learning for <u>Year 2 Autumn Term</u>.
- It's split up into <u>blocks</u>, with each <u>small step</u> covered on one or two pages.

There are questions on all the <u>key content</u>, giving great practice for every step.

We've included plenty of <u>pictorial</u> questions throughout.

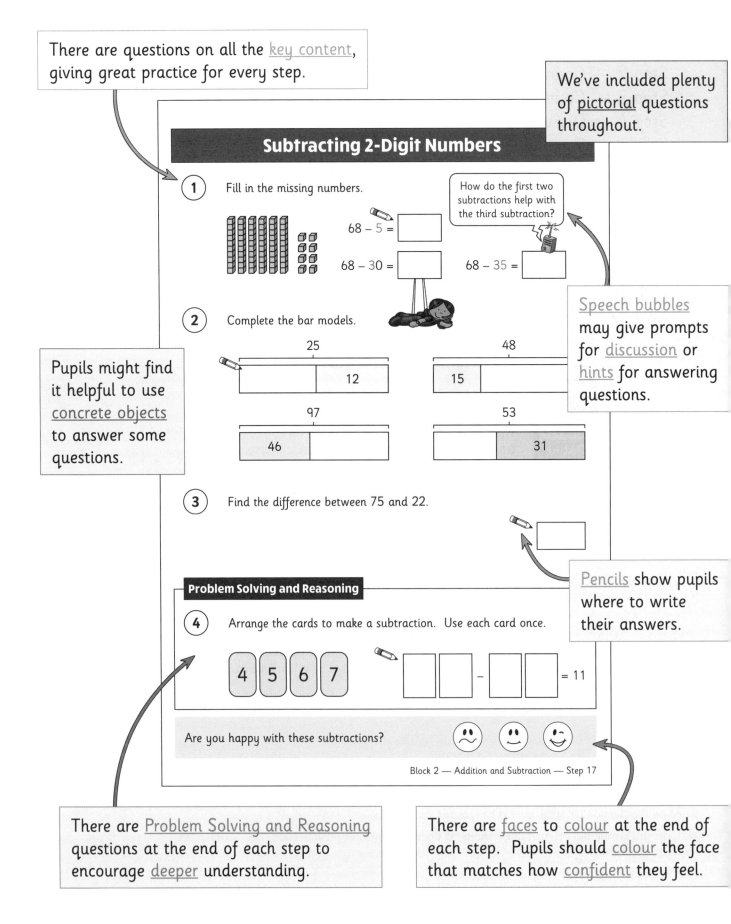

Subtracting 2-Digit Numbers

1 Fill in the missing numbers.

68 – 5 = ⬚

68 – 30 = ⬚

68 – 35 = ⬚

How do the first two subtractions help with the third subtraction?

<u>Speech bubbles</u> may give prompts for <u>discussion</u> or <u>hints</u> for answering questions.

2 Complete the bar models.

25 | 12

48 | 15

97 | 46

53 | 31

Pupils might find it helpful to use <u>concrete objects</u> to answer some questions.

3 Find the difference between 75 and 22.

<u>Pencils</u> show pupils where to write their answers.

Problem Solving and Reasoning

4 Arrange the cards to make a subtraction. Use each card once.

4 5 6 7

⬚⬚ – ⬚⬚ = 11

Are you happy with these subtractions?

Block 2 — Addition and Subtraction — Step 17

There are <u>Problem Solving and Reasoning</u> questions at the end of each step to encourage <u>deeper</u> understanding.

There are <u>faces</u> to <u>colour</u> at the end of each step. Pupils should <u>colour</u> the face that matches how <u>confident</u> they feel.

Numbers to 20

1 Write the number and the word for each picture.

number: [ ]   word: [ ]

number: [ ]   word: [ ]

2 Write these words as numbers.

twenty [ ]   twelve [ ]   eleven [ ]

3 Fill in the missing word and number on the number track.

| fourteen | 15 | sixteen | 17 | | |

Problem Solving and Reasoning

4 Zahira is saying her address.

Has Zahira said it wrong?
If yes, what should she say instead?

I live at threeteen Castle Road.

13

Can you write the numbers to 20 in words?

Counting Objects

1 How many coins are there? Tick the correct number.

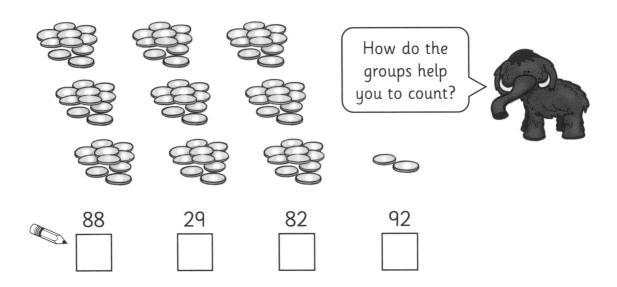

How do the groups help you to count?

88	29	82	92
☐	☐	☐	☐

2 Complete the sentence about the number shown.

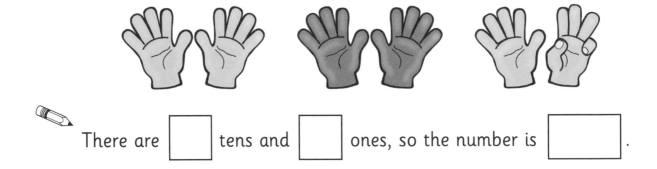

There are ☐ tens and ☐ ones, so the number is ☐.

3 Circle the picture that shows 32.

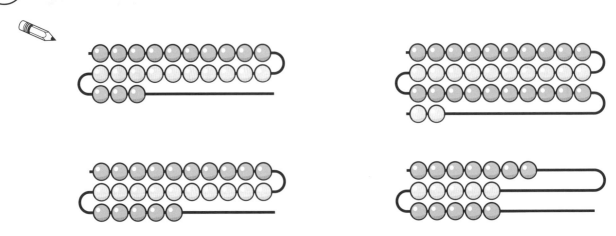

4 What number is shown?

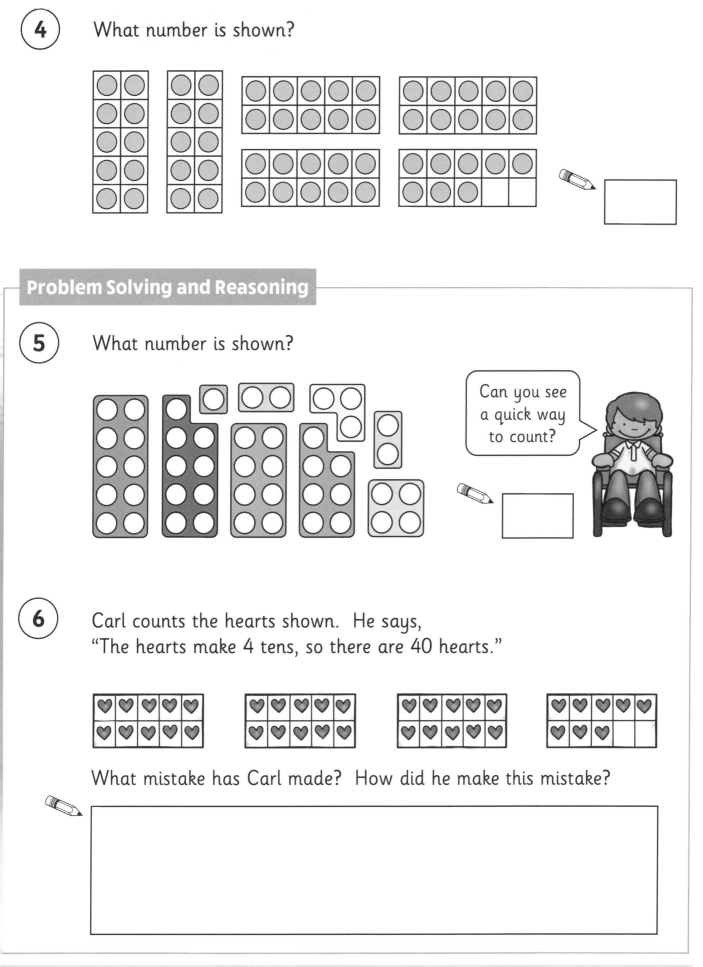

Problem Solving and Reasoning

5 What number is shown?

Can you see a quick way to count?

6 Carl counts the hearts shown. He says,
"The hearts make 4 tens, so there are 40 hearts."

What mistake has Carl made? How did he make this mistake?

Can you count to 100 using groups of 10?

Tens and Ones

1 How many tens are shown below? How many ones are shown?

☐ tens ☐ ones

2 How many crayons are there?

3 Draw a ring around exactly 43 carrots.

Problem Solving and Reasoning

4 Joe needs 39 pencils. How many more full boxes does he need?

I have these pencils.

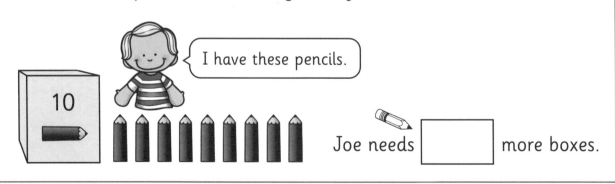

Joe needs ☐ more boxes.

Can you spot the tens and ones in numbers?

Place Value Charts

1 How many tens and ones are there in the place value chart?

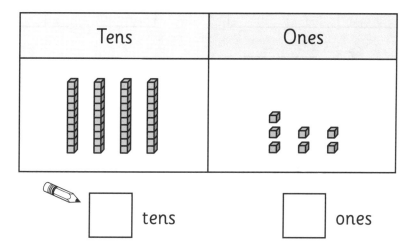

▱ [ ] tens   [ ] ones

2 Draw the missing blocks to complete the place value chart.

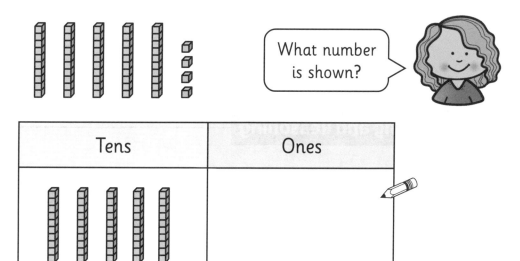

What number is shown?

3 Write digits in the place value charts to show each number.

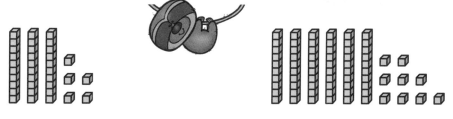

Tens	Ones

Tens	Ones

6

4) What numbers are shown by the place value charts?

T	O
2	6

The number is ⬚ .

T	O
7	3

The number is ⬚ .

5) Complete the sentence and place value chart for the number 30.

There are ⬚ tens and ⬚ ones.

T	O

How would the base 10 look?

Problem Solving and Reasoning

6) Erin writes the number on the left in a place value chart.

T	O
8	2

Is Erin correct?
Tick your answer and write how you know.

Yes ⬚ No ⬚

Do you understand place value charts?

Block 1 — Place Value — Step 4Block 1 — Place Value — Step 4

Partitioning Numbers

1 How many tens and ones are in the number shown?

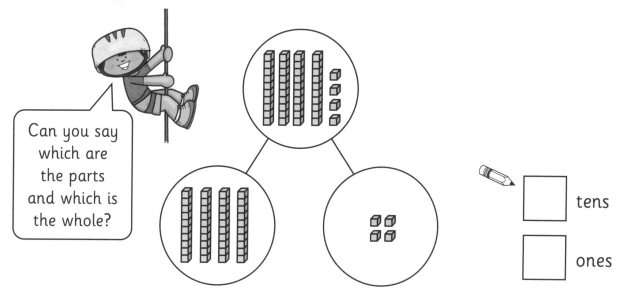

Can you say which are the parts and which is the whole?

☐ tens

☐ ones

2 Complete the part-whole models with base 10.

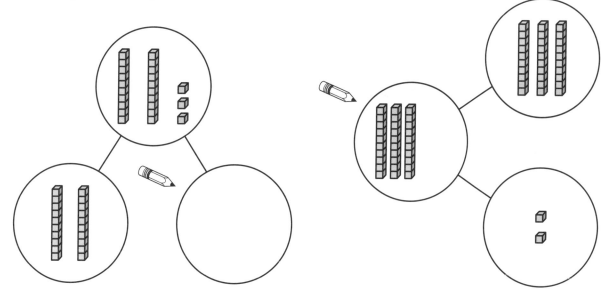

3 Write the missing number in the part-whole model.

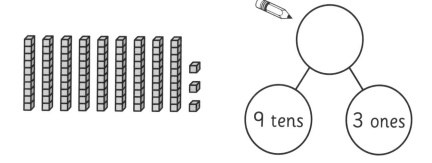

9 tens   3 ones

4 Complete the part-whole models.

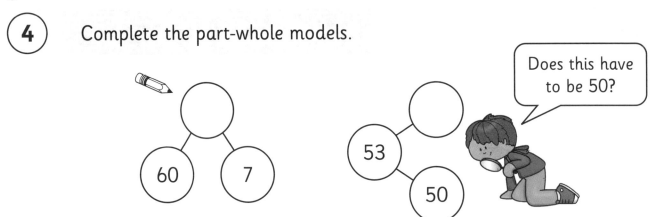

Does this have to be 50?

5 Use the part-whole model to partition the number shown into tens and ones.

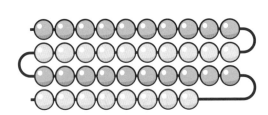

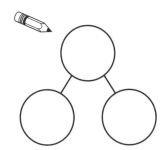

Problem Solving and Reasoning

6 Sadiq partitions the number shown using a part-whole model.

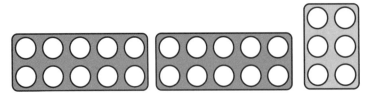

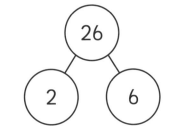

What has Sadiq done incorrectly?

Can you partition numbers into tens and ones?

Writing Numbers in Words

1 Fill in the missing words.

The number with five tens is fifty. The number with six tens is

[ ]. The number with seven tens is [ ].

2 Complete the part-whole model. Then write the number in words.

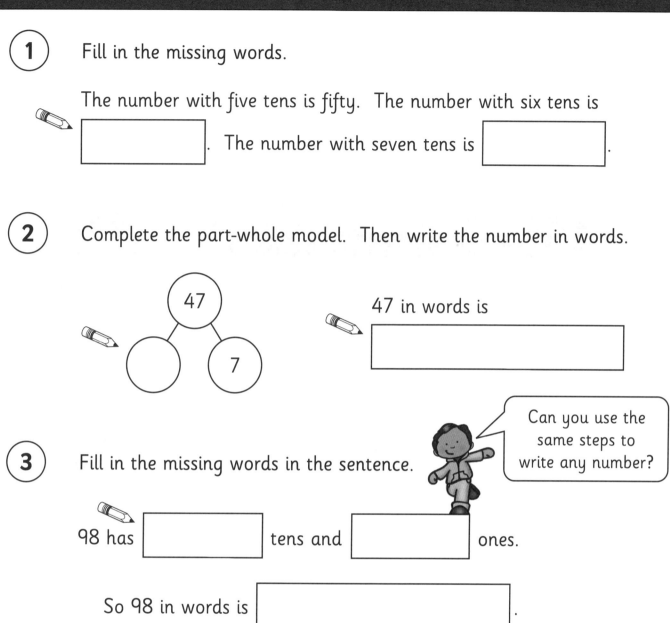

47 in words is

[ ]

> Can you use the same steps to write any number?

3 Fill in the missing words in the sentence.

98 has [ ] tens and [ ] ones.

So 98 in words is [ ].

Problem Solving and Reasoning

4 Circle any words you would say when counting from 0 to 100.

| one hundred | nineteen | thirty-ten | twelve |
| twenty-eleven | eighty-one | fiveteen | seventy-six |

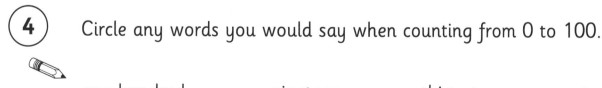
Can you write the numbers up to 100 in words?

More Partitioning Numbers

1 Draw lines to match each picture to the base 10.

2 Fill in these part-whole models with base 10.

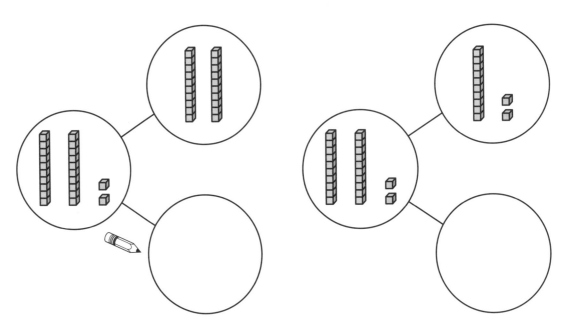

3 Use the base 10 to fill in the gap in each sentence.

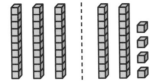

54 can be partitioned into

30 and ☐.

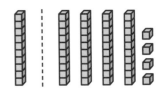

54 can be partitioned into

10 and ☐.

4 Write in the missing numbers.

Can you think of more ways to partition 86?

(86) — ( ) (16)

(86) — ( ) (76)

Problem Solving and Reasoning

5 Sofia the squirrel partitions 75 in 3 part-whole models.

(75) — (70) (5)

(75) — (60) (15)

(75) — (50) (25)

Describe the pattern between each part-whole model.

6 Ace the acorn partitions 48 into 2 tens and 28 ones.

48 can also be written as 228.

What mistake has Ace made?

How did you find these questions?

Writing Numbers in Expanded Form

(1) Complete the number sentences to match the picture.

4 tens + ☐ ones = 48   ☐ = 40 + ☐

(2) Fill in the number sentence to match the part-whole model.

82
80   2

☐ = ☐ + ☐

Problem Solving and Reasoning

(3) Cross out the number sentences that are wrong.

62 = 6 + 2   62 = 12 + 50   60 + 2 = 62

55 = 40 + 15   55 = 50 + 50   50 + 5 = 55

(4) Two dogs are arguing about how to write 34 as a number sentence.

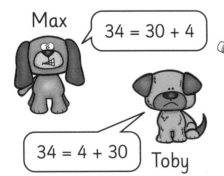

Max — 34 = 30 + 4

34 = 4 + 30 — Toby

Is Max correct, or Toby, or both? Say why.

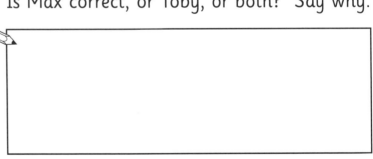

Are you confident using "+" and "="?

The Number Line (Tens)

1 Complete these number lines and the sentence about them.

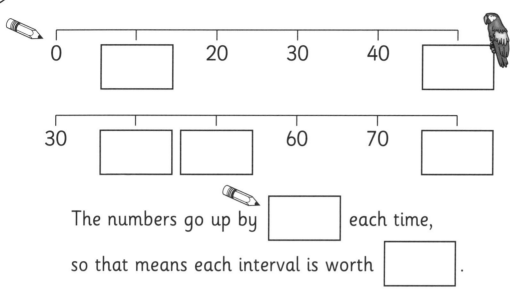

0 [ ] 20 30 40 [ ]

30 [ ] [ ] 60 70 [ ]

The numbers go up by [ ] each time,

so that means each interval is worth [ ] .

2 Circle the number that is marked by the cross on the number line.

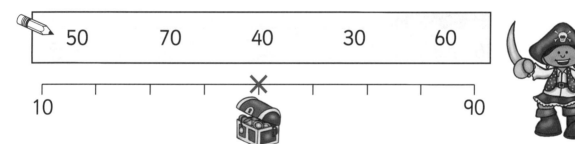

50   70   40   30   60

10 ✕ 90

Problem Solving and Reasoning

3 Complete these number lines so that
three of the numbers appear on both lines.

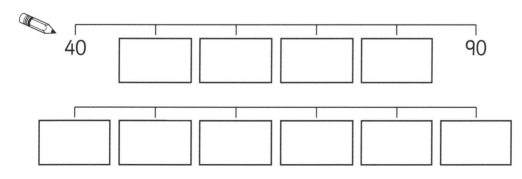

40 [ ] [ ] [ ] [ ] 90

[ ] [ ] [ ] [ ] [ ] [ ]

Can you label 10s on a number line?

The Number Line (Ones)

1 Fill in the gaps on the number line.

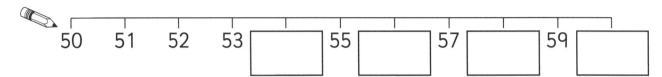

50   51   52   53   [ ]   55   [ ]   57   [ ]   59   [ ]

2 Draw an arrow to show where 73 is on the number line.

67   77

3 Tick the number lines that finish on the same number.

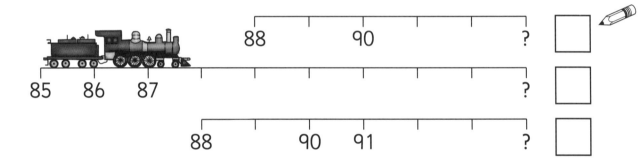

88   90   ?   [ ]

85   86   87   ?   [ ]

88   90   91   ?   [ ]

Problem Solving and Reasoning

4 Leon circles part of the number line to show where 29 is.

23   30

What has Leon done wrong?

[   ]

Can you label ones on a number line?

Estimating Numbers

1 Draw a cross on each number line to estimate where the number 5 is.

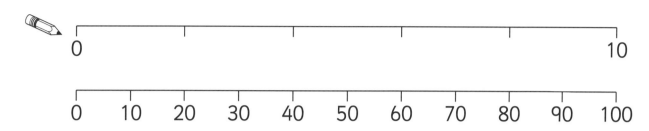

2 Estimate the numbers that the bananas are on.

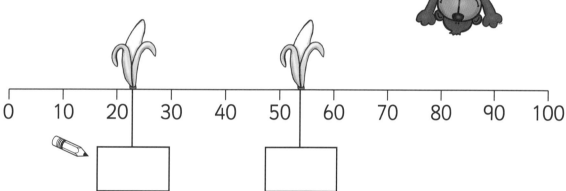

---

3 Hugo draws a cross to mark 68 on the number line shown.

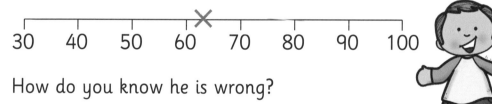

How do you know he is wrong?

Can you estimate numbers on a number line?

Comparing Objects

1 Fill in each box with the number of carrots Clive and Austin have. Then circle the correct word in the sentence below.

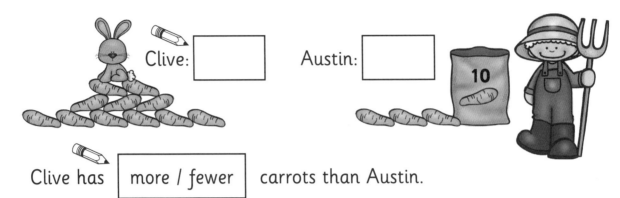

Clive: ☐   Austin: ☐

Clive has | more / fewer | carrots than Austin.

2 Circle the correct symbol and word to compare the numbers of apples and pears.

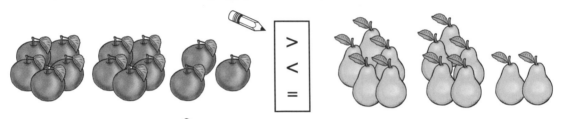

The number of apples is | greater / less | than the number of pears.

Problem Solving and Reasoning

3 Magda points at where she thinks she sees more doughnuts.

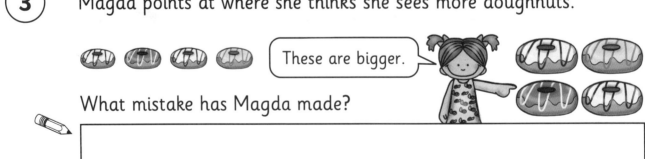

These are bigger.

What mistake has Magda made?

☐

Can you compare numbers of objects?

Comparing Numbers

1 Circle all the numbers greater than 26.

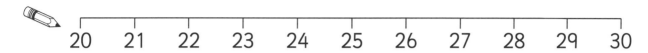

20   21   22   23   24   25   26   27   28   29   30

2 Choose the correct answer from the blue box to fill in each gap.
You can use the number line to help.

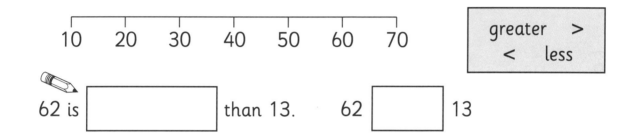

10   20   30   40   50   60   70

| greater | > |
| < | less |

62 is [   ] than 13.   62 [   ] 13

3 Write <, > or = in each box.

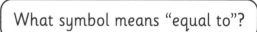
What symbol means "equal to"?

49 [   ] 44   43 [   ] 34   45 [   ] 46

39 [   ] 30 + 9   35 [   ] 12 + 24   30 + 13 [   ] 33

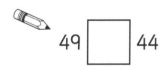

Problem Solving and Reasoning

4 What number is Ringo the doughnut thinking of?

My number is less than 71, greater than 59,
and the number of tens is equal to the number of ones.

Ringo's number is [   ].

Are you able to compare numbers?

Ordering Numbers

1 Tick the box below the group with the most balls.

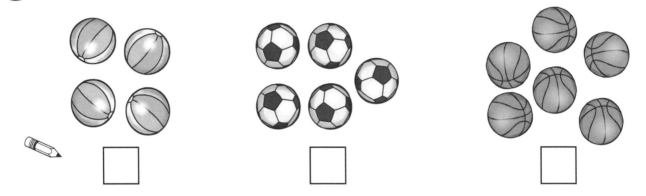

☐ ☐ ☐

2 Here are four numbers. Put a tick next to the smallest number and a cross next to the greatest number.

43 ☐

5 tens ☐

3 Write these numbers in order, from smallest to greatest.

58   56   92   39   29

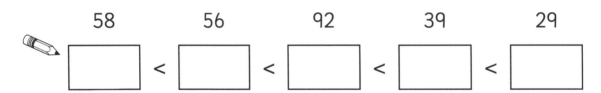

☐ < ☐ < ☐ < ☐ < ☐

Problem Solving and Reasoning

4 Daniel compares three numbers.

Rewrite Daniel's statement correctly.

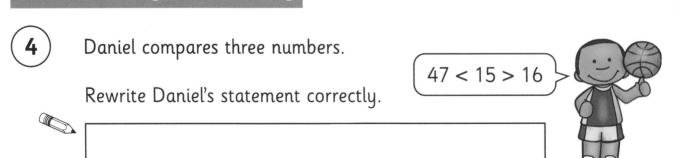

47 < 15 > 16

☐

Can you put a set of numbers in order?

Counting in Twos, Fives and Tens

1 Write the numbers shown. What is the next number in the pattern?

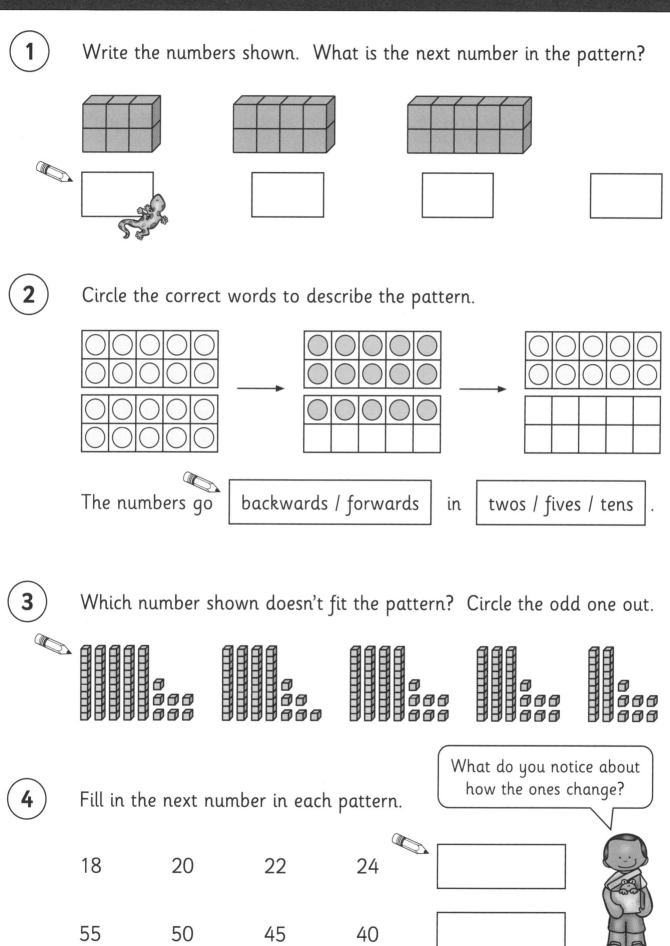

2 Circle the correct words to describe the pattern.

The numbers go | backwards / forwards | in | twos / fives / tens |.

3 Which number shown doesn't fit the pattern? Circle the odd one out.

What do you notice about how the ones change?

4 Fill in the next number in each pattern.

18   20   22   24

55   50   45   40

5 Fill in the missing word and number on the number track.

| thirteen | 23 | thirty-three | 43 | | |

6 For each row, cross out the number that does not fit the pattern.

40	45	50	55	60	70
32	30	28	26	25	24
96	86	77	76	66	56

7 Fill in the missing numbers on the number tracks.

| 15 | | | 45 | 55 | | |

| | | 60 | | 70 | | |

Problem Solving and Reasoning

8 Lian is counting in 10s. Tick any statement that is true.

If I start from 7, all the numbers I say will be odd. ☐

If I start from 30, all the numbers I say will be even. ☐

9 Is Eve counting in 5s or 10s? Tick the correct answer.

Every number I say ends in 5.

Eve is counting in 5s. ☐

Eve is counting in 10s. ☐

Can you count in 2s, 5s and 10s?

Counting in Threes

1 Write the numbers shown. What is the next number in the pattern?

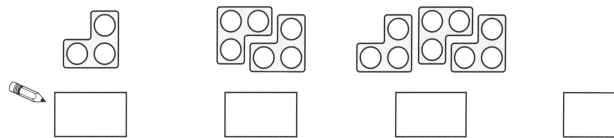

2 Count in 3s from the circled numbers. Circle each number you say.

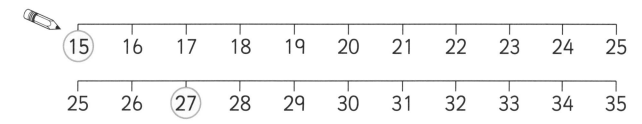

3 Fill in the missing numbers on the number track.

Problem Solving and Reasoning

4 Boris is counting in threes. 63, 66, 69, 73, 76, 79

Is Boris correct?
Tick your answer and write how you know. Yes ☐ No ☐

Can you count forwards and backwards in 3s?

Number Bonds to 10

1 Which bond to 10 does the ten frame show?

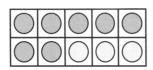   ☐ + ☐ = 10

Is there another way to write your answer?

2 Complete the number bond to 10.

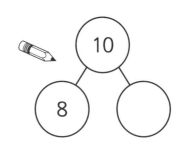

3 Complete the bar models.

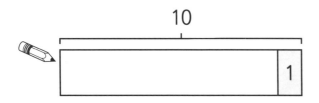

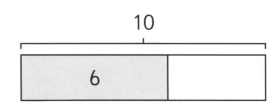

4 Complete the number bonds to 10.

4 + ☐ = 10   2 + ☐ = 10   ☐ + 0 = 10

Problem Solving and Reasoning

5 George is describing a number bond to 10.

Write a number sentence for his bond.

☐ + ☐ = ☐

My ten frame shows the same number of green and yellow counters.

Do you know the number bonds to 10?

Number Bonds up to 20

1 Look at the ten frames. Then complete the number sentence.

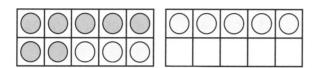

$7 + \boxed{} = \boxed{}$

2 Look at the bonds to 10. Then complete the bonds to 20.

$\boxed{1 + 9 = 10}$

$1 + \boxed{} = 20$

$\boxed{4 + 6 = 10}$

$\boxed{} + 6 = 20$

What do you notice?

3 Maggie makes a fact family to match the bar model.

Which fact is **wrong**? Circle your answer.

20

| 13 | 7 |

$20 = 13 + 7$ $20 - 13 = 7$

$20 - 7 = 13$ $13 - 7 = 20$

Problem Solving and Reasoning

4 Complete the fact family.

Do you know any other facts in this fact family?

$\boxed{} + 12 = 16$ $16 - 4 = \boxed{}$

$\boxed{} - 12 = \boxed{}$ $12 + \boxed{} = \boxed{}$

Can you make fact families within 20?

Related Number Facts

1 Complete the number sentences to match the blocks.

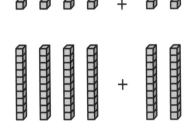 +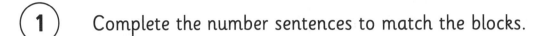

4 ones + ☐ ones = 6 ones

 +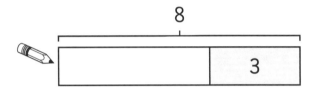

4 tens + ☐ tens = ☐ tens

2 Complete the bar models.

Do the bar models show related facts?

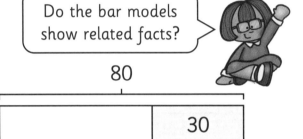

8
	3

80
	30

3 Circle the fact related to the number sentence in the box.

7 + 2 = 9

70 + 2 = 90   70 + 20 = 900

70 + 20 = 9   70 + 20 = 90

Problem Solving and Reasoning

4 Parvesh is talking about related facts.

Explain why he is wrong.

I know 2 + 5 = 7, so 20 + 50 = 700.

Can you spot related facts?

Number Bonds up to 100

1 Complete the number sentences to match the blocks.

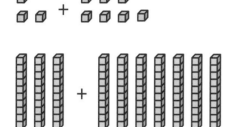

[ ] ones + [ ] ones = 10

[ ] tens + [ ] tens = [ ]

2 Use the hundred square to complete the sentences.

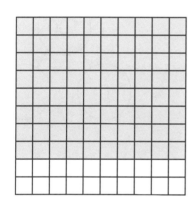

There are [ ] pink squares

and [ ] white squares.

So [ ] + [ ] =100.

Is there a quick way to count the squares?

3 Use the number bonds to 10 to write number bonds to 100.

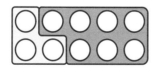

3 + 7 = 10

[ ] + 70 = 100

2 + 8 = 10

[ ] + [ ] = 100

1 + 9 = 10

[ ] + [ ] = [ ]

(4) Ari shows a number bond to 100 on the hundred square.

Circle **all** the number sentences that match.

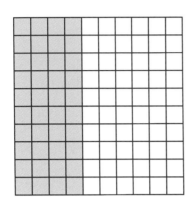

40 + 6 = 100   100 + 60 = 40

40 + 60 = 100   4 + 60 = 10

10 + 40 = 60   60 + 40 = 100

(5) Complete the number bonds to 100.

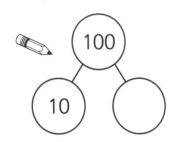   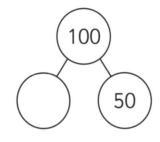   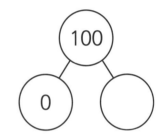

Problem Solving and Reasoning

(6) There are 100 beads on the frame. Some are covered up.

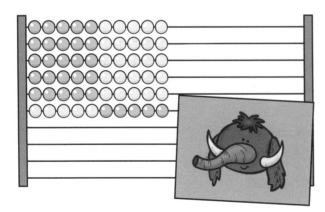

How many beads are covered?

 beads

Write the number bond to 100.

☐ + ☐ = 100

Can you use 10s to make bonds to 100?

Adding and Subtracting Ones

1 Use the number shapes to fill in the number sentences.

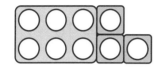

9 – 1 = ☐   9 – 2 = ☐   9 – 3 = ☐

2 Fill in the missing numbers on the number track.

		15	16		

Can you think of a number sentence for each number you fill in?

3 Complete the number sentences.

50 + 1 = ☐   74 – 4 = ☐   31 + 3 = ☐

81 + 2 = ☐   99 – 2 = ☐

Problem Solving and Reasoning

4 Charles is trying to solve the problem in the box.   98 – ? = 95

Write a bond to 8 he could use to help solve the problem.

☐ + ☐ = ☐

Can you add and subtract using 1s?

Adding (Making 10)

1 Fill in the missing numbers to match the ten frames.

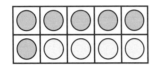 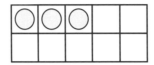

$6 +$ ☐ $= 10 +$ ☐

2 Use the partition and the number line to find $8 + 6$.

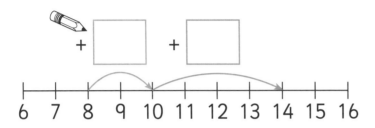

+ ☐ + ☐

6 7 8 9 10 11 12 13 14 15 16

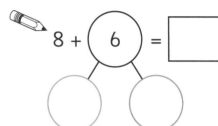

$8 +$ (6) $=$ ☐

3 Follow the steps to find $7 + 9$.

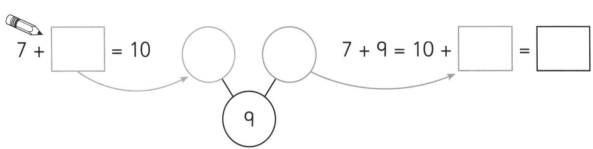

$7 +$ ☐ $= 10$ $7 + 9 = 10 +$ ☐ $=$ ☐

9

Problem Solving and Reasoning

4 Theresa is working out $9 + 9$.   I will add 4 first, then 5.

Is there an easier way to do this sum?

How did you find these additions?

Adding Three Numbers

1 Use the number shapes to complete the additions.

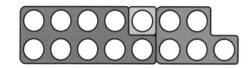   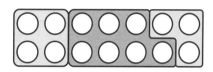

$9 + 1 + 5 =$ ☐ $4 + 7 + 3 =$ ☐

2 Complete the bar models.

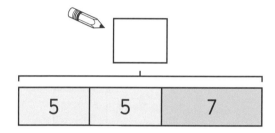   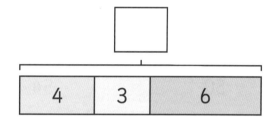

3 Work out these sums.

$7 + 2 + 6 =$ ☐ $4 + 5 + 8 =$ ☐ $3 + 8 + 9 =$ ☐

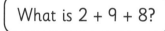

Problem Solving and Reasoning

4 Peter needs help with an addition.

What would you tell him to do first and why?

 What is 2 + 9 + 8?

Can you add three numbers together?

Adding (To 10s)

1 The beads show 36. Fill in the missing numbers.

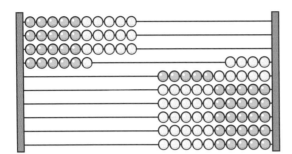

I can move ☐ beads to make 40.

So 36 + ☐ = ☐ .

2 Fill in the missing numbers.

+ ☐

Can you see a number bond to 10?

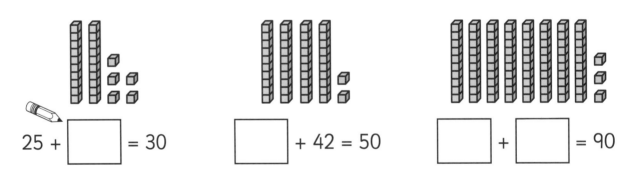

50   54

3 Use the base 10 to complete the additions.

25 + ☐ = 30

☐ + 42 = 50

☐ + ☐ = 90

Problem Solving and Reasoning

4 Martina is thinking of a number.

What could Martina's number be?

I need to add 6 to get my number to the next 10.

Can you add to the next 10?

Adding (Across 10s)

1 The blocks show 49 + 3. Fill in the missing numbers to match.

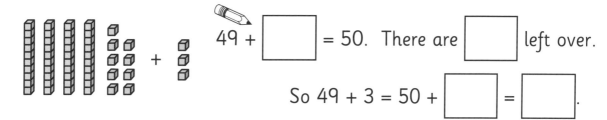

49 + ☐ = 50. There are ☐ left over.

So 49 + 3 = 50 + ☐ = ☐ .

2 Use the number lines to work out the sums.

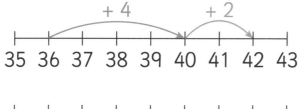

36 + 6 = ☐

58 + 7 = ☐

3 Complete the addition using the part-whole model.

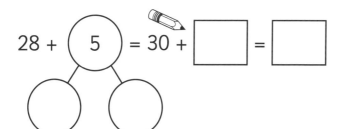

28 + (5) = 30 + ☐ = ☐

Where does the 30 come from?

Problem Solving and Reasoning

4 Molly is talking about additions.

44 + 9 is loads easier than 9 + 44!

Do you agree or would you say something else?

Can you add across 10s?

Subtraction Within 20

1 Use the number shapes to complete the subtraction.

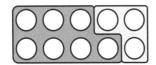

$14 - 7 = 10 - \boxed{} = \boxed{}$

2 Use the number lines to work out the subtractions.

```
├──┼──┼──┼──┼──┼──┼──┼──┼──┼──┤
6   7   8   9  10  11  12  13  14  15  16
```

$15 - 6 = \boxed{}$

```
├──┼──┼──┼──┼──┼──┼──┼──┼──┼──┤
4   5   6   7   8   9  10  11  12  13  14
```

$12 - \boxed{} = 7$

3 Fill in the missing numbers to work out $13 - 8$.

$13 - \boxed{} = 10$ ◯ ◯ $13 - 8 = 10 - \boxed{} = \boxed{}$

⑧

Why is it helpful to use number bonds to 10?

Problem Solving and Reasoning

4 Shelly has 15 sweets. She gives 7 to James and 2 to Samira.

How many sweets does Shelly have left over? $\boxed{}$ sweets

How are you at subtracting across 10?

Subtracting (From 10s)

1 Fill in the missing numbers to match the hundred square.

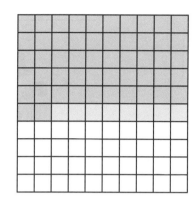

There are [ ] blue squares

and [ ] orange squares.

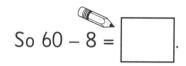

So 60 − 8 = [ ] .

2 Use the ten frame to work out the subtraction.

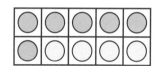

10 − 4 = [ ]

♪ How are these ♪ ♫ subtractions similar?

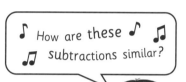

Now fill in the similar subtractions.

20 − 4 = [ ]   30 − 4 = [ ]   40 − 4 = [ ]

3 Use the numbers from the box to complete the subtractions.

70 − [ ] = 65   90 − [ ] = 87   40 − [ ] = 39

| 1 |
| 5 |
| 3 |

Problem Solving and Reasoning

4 Circle two facts you could use to help solve 20 − 8.

20 + 8 = 28   18 − 2 = 16   8 + 12 = 20   2 + 8 = 10

Can you subtract from 10s?

Subtracting (Across 10s)

1 Complete the subtraction to match the blocks.

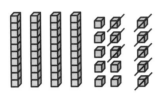

55 – 8 = ☐

Why have only
4 tens been grouped?

2 Use the number lines to work out the subtractions.

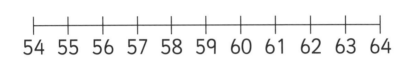
54 55 56 57 58 59 60 61 62 63 64

64 – 7 = ☐

31 32 33 34 35 36 37 38 39 40 41

41 – 8 = ☐

3 Use subtraction to complete these part-whole models.

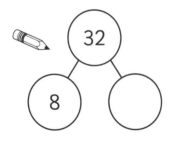

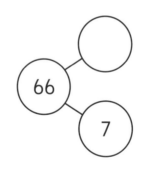

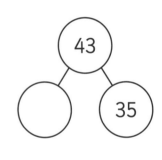

Problem Solving and Reasoning

4 Complete each subtraction to make them all have the same answer.

83 – 5   87 – ☐   ☐ – 4   85 – ☐

Can you subtract across a 10?

Finding 10 More and 10 Less

1 Complete the sentences.

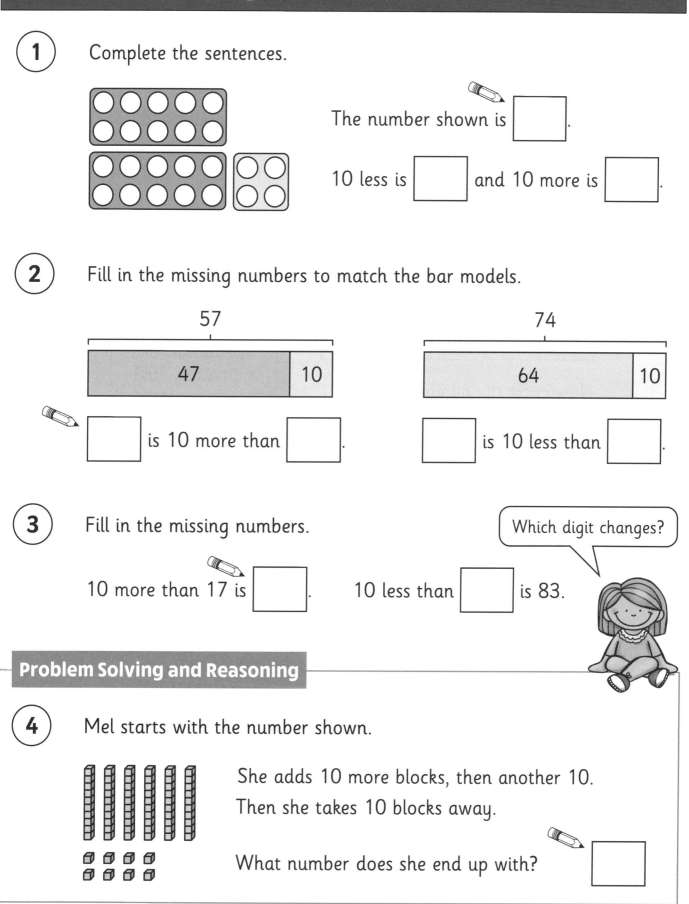

The number shown is [ ].

10 less is [ ] and 10 more is [ ].

2 Fill in the missing numbers to match the bar models.

57
| 47 | 10 |

[ ] is 10 more than [ ].

74
| 64 | 10 |

[ ] is 10 less than [ ].

3 Fill in the missing numbers.

Which digit changes?

10 more than 17 is [ ].   10 less than [ ] is 83.

Problem Solving and Reasoning

4 Mel starts with the number shown.

She adds 10 more blocks, then another 10.
Then she takes 10 blocks away.

What number does she end up with? [ ]

Are you happy with all that?

Adding and Subtracting Tens

1 Fill in the missing numbers to work out 11 + 20.

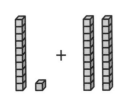

20 has ☐ tens, so I should add ☐ and then add ☐ again. So 11 + 20 = ☐.

2 Complete the number track by counting in 20s.

		58	78	

Now circle the number on the number track that is 40 less than 78.

Do the ones matter when adding and subtracting 10s?

3 Complete the calculations.

80 – 30 = ☐   40 + 37 = ☐   ☐ – 20 = 75

Problem Solving and Reasoning

4 Fill in the gaps on the number line.

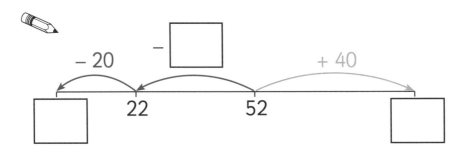

Can you add and subtract 10s?

Adding 2-Digit Numbers

1 Fill in the missing numbers to match the blocks.

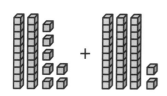

There are ☐ tens and ☐ ones in total.

So 27 + 32 = ☐ .

2 Noora and Micah each have some cookies.

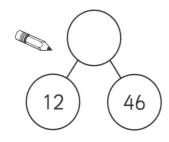 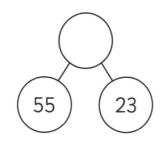 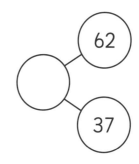

Noora   Micah

How many cookies do they have altogether?

☐ cookies

3 Use addition to complete these part-whole models.

12   46   55   23   62   37

Problem Solving and Reasoning

4 Clem and Josh went on holiday. They took 56 photos altogether. Clem took 25 of the photos.

How many of the photos did Josh take?

☐ photos

Are you happy adding 2-digit numbers?

Adding 2-Digit Numbers (Across 10)

1 Work out these additions.

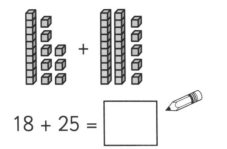

18 + 25 = ☐

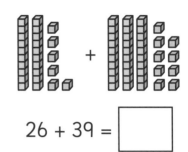

26 + 39 = ☐

2 Fill in the tens digit to complete each bar model.

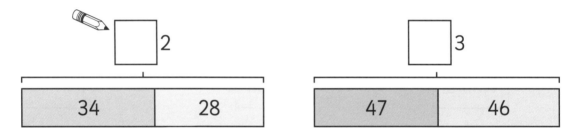

☐ 2

| 34 | 28 |

☐ 3

| 47 | 46 |

3 Draw a line from the box to each addition that makes 82.

24 + 61   82   59 + 33

32 + 52   64 + 18

46 + 36   57 + 27

Problem Solving and Reasoning

4 Polly is working out 36 + 57.

What has Polly done wrong?

The answer is 83.

How did these additions go?

Subtracting 2-Digit Numbers

1 Fill in the missing numbers.

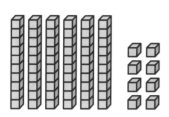

$68 - 5 = \boxed{}$

How do the first two subtractions help with the third subtraction?

$68 - 30 = \boxed{}$

$68 - 35 = \boxed{}$

2 Complete the bar models.

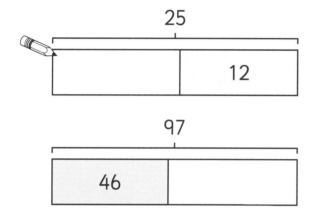

25

| | 12 |

48

| 15 | |

97

| 46 | |

53

| | 31 |

3 Find the difference between 75 and 22.

$\boxed{}$

Problem Solving and Reasoning

4 Arrange the cards to make a subtraction. Use each card once.

4 5 6 7

 $\boxed{}\boxed{} - \boxed{}\boxed{} = 11$

Are you happy with these subtractions?

Subtracting 2-Digit Numbers (Across 10)

1 Use the base 10 to work out the subtraction.

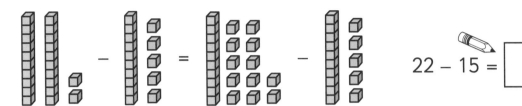

22 – 15 =

2 Fill in the missing numbers in the bar models.

72

45

83

27

3 Work out these subtractions.

35 – 18 =

42 – 27 =

54 – 16 =

64 – 39 =

Problem Solving and Reasoning

4 Jai has tried to do a subtraction.

What has Jai done wrong?

I know that
6 – 2 = 4, so
52 – 36 = 24.

Can you subtract 2-digit numbers across a ten?

Mixed Calculations

1 Complete the calculations. Use the base 10 to help you.

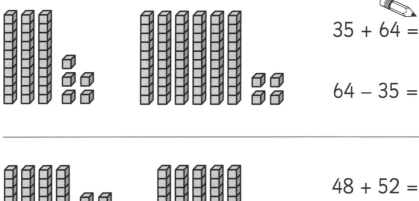

$35 + 64 =$ ▢

$64 - 35 =$ ▢

$48 + 52 =$ ▢

$52 - 48 =$ ▢

2 What is the difference between 25 and 17?

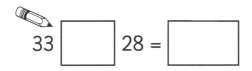

3 Georgina has 33 red blocks and 28 blue blocks.

How many blocks does she have altogether?

33 ▢ $28 =$ ▢

How did you know which symbol to use?

4 Daniel has 64 crayons. He gives 27 crayons to Heather.

How many crayons does Daniel have left?

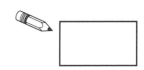

5 Mai bought a book for £8 and a toy for £39.

How much did she spend altogether?

 £8  £39

 £

6 Lily's great-grandmother is 92 years old.
Her grandmother is 35 years younger.

How old is Lily's grandmother?

 years old

Problem Solving and Reasoning

7 Jenny and Lee are playing a game.
They each need 45 points to win.

 I need 11 more points to win.

 I have 18 fewer points than Jenny.

Jenny

Lee

How many points do Jenny and Lee have?

 Jenny: points   Lee: points

How did you do?

Comparing Calculations

1 Write < or > to compare the additions and subtractions.
You can use the base 10 to help you.

34 + 17 ☐ 45 + 23

34 − 17 ☐ 45 − 23

45 − 17 ☐ 34 − 23

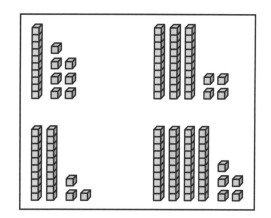

2 Arash and Milly each have 34 socks. Arash loses 7 socks.
Milly loses 18 socks. Who has more socks left?

Do you need to
do a calculation?

3 Compare the calculations by writing < or >.

56 + 27 ☐ 56 + 18   56 − 27 ☐ 56 − 18

Problem Solving and Reasoning

4 Jay is comparing two additions.

28 + 54 is greater
than 17 + 54

How does he know this without doing a calculation?

Have you got the hang of comparing?

Missing Number Problems

1 Draw the ones to complete the part-whole model and addition.

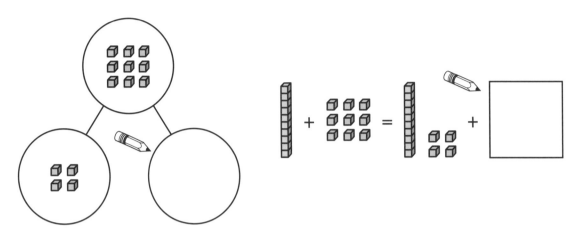

2 Complete the part-whole model and the number sentences.

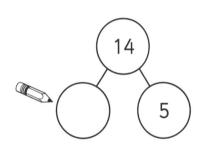

$35 - 14 = \boxed{} - 9$

$49 - 14 = \boxed{} - 5$

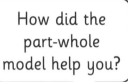

How did the part-whole model help you?

3 Work out the missing numbers.

$15 + 6 = 20 + \boxed{}$

$42 + 14 = \boxed{} + 24$

Problem Solving and Reasoning

4 Sarah completed this number sentence, then spilled sauce on it.

$$57 + \text{⬤} = 51 + \text{⬤}$$

Find two pairs of numbers that could be under the sauce.

 $\boxed{}$ and $\boxed{}$ $\boxed{}$ and $\boxed{}$

Can you find those missing numbers?

Naming Shapes

1 Write how many of each shape there are.

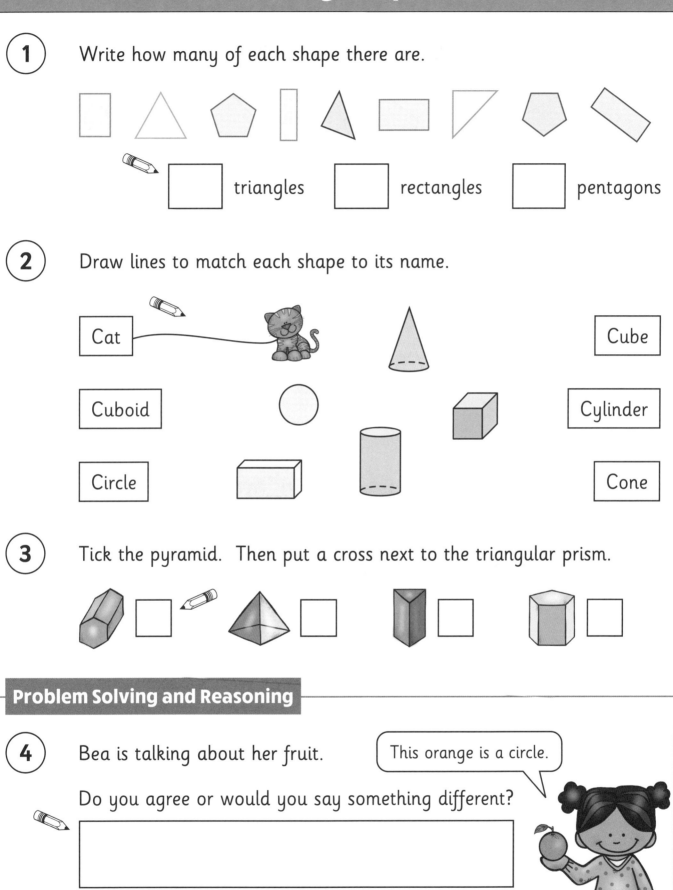

☐ triangles   ☐ rectangles   ☐ pentagons

2 Draw lines to match each shape to its name.

Cat

Cuboid

Circle

Cube

Cylinder

Cone

3 Tick the pyramid. Then put a cross next to the triangular prism.

Problem Solving and Reasoning

4 Bea is talking about her fruit.

This orange is a circle.

Do you agree or would you say something different?

How well do you know 2D and 3D shapes?

Counting Sides of 2D Shapes

1 How many sides does each shape have?

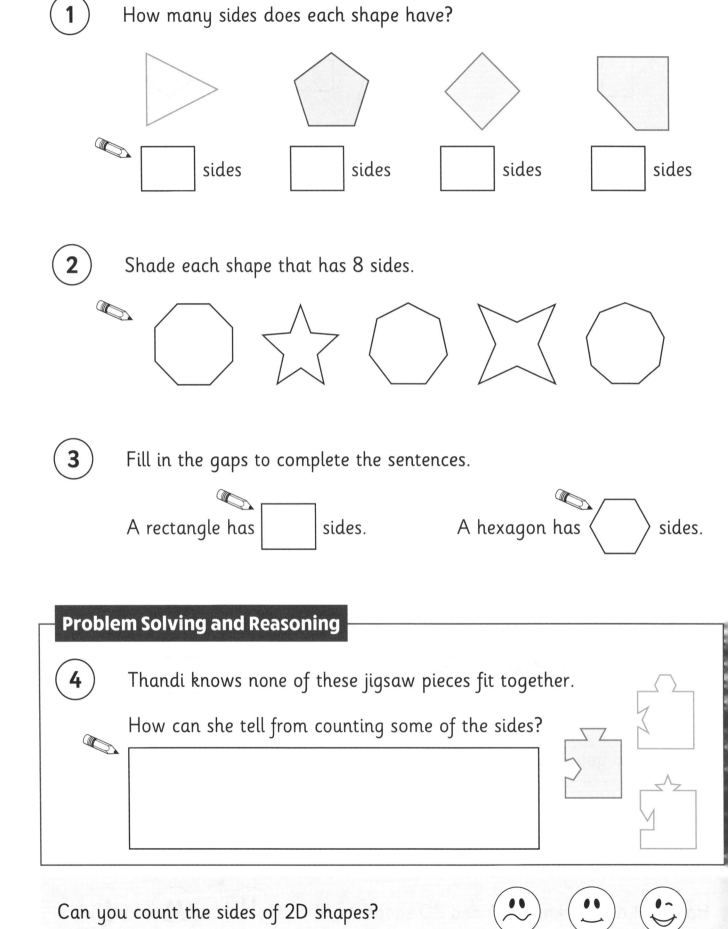

☐ sides   ☐ sides   ☐ sides   ☐ sides

2 Shade each shape that has 8 sides.

3 Fill in the gaps to complete the sentences.

A rectangle has ☐ sides.   A hexagon has ⬡ sides.

Problem Solving and Reasoning

4 Thandi knows none of these jigsaw pieces fit together.

How can she tell from counting some of the sides?

Can you count the sides of 2D shapes?

Counting Vertices of 2D Shapes

1 Tick the shape with the correct number of vertices.

3 vertices   5 vertices

2 Draw lines to match each shape to its number of vertices.

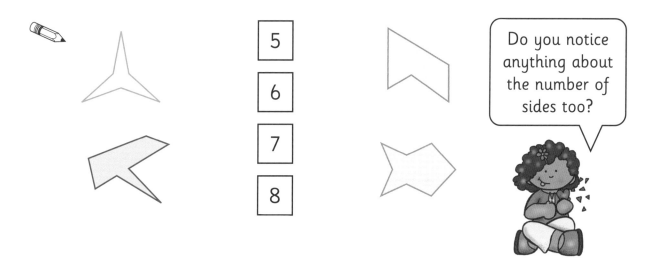

Do you notice anything about the number of sides too?

Problem Solving and Reasoning

3 If you join 4 dots to make a shape, will the shape have 4 vertices?

Try with the dots below then tick the answer.

Always ☐
Sometimes ☐
Never ☐

Can you count the vertices of 2D shapes?

Drawing Shapes

1 Fill in the missing numbers. Then finish drawing the square.

A square has:

[ ] vertices

[ ] sides

Why is it important to use a ruler?

2 Draw a bigger rectangle.

3 Kathy has drawn a triangle. Draw two different triangles.

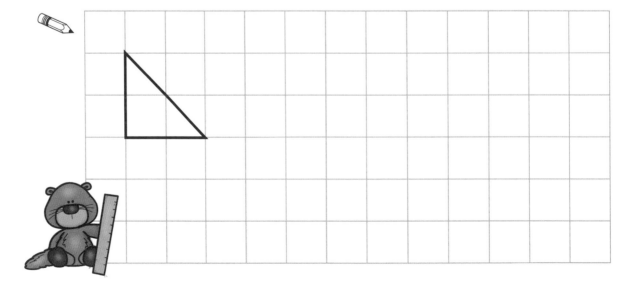

4 Complete the shapes.

Pentagon

Hexagon

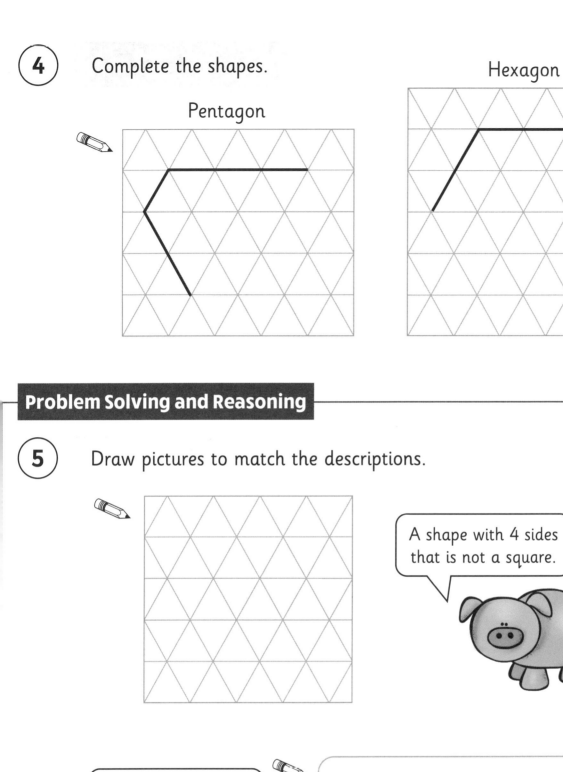

Problem Solving and Reasoning

5 Draw pictures to match the descriptions.

A shape with 4 sides that is not a square.

A small triangle inside a big triangle.

How did you find drawing 2D shapes?

Symmetry

1 Tick each shape that has a vertical line of symmetry.

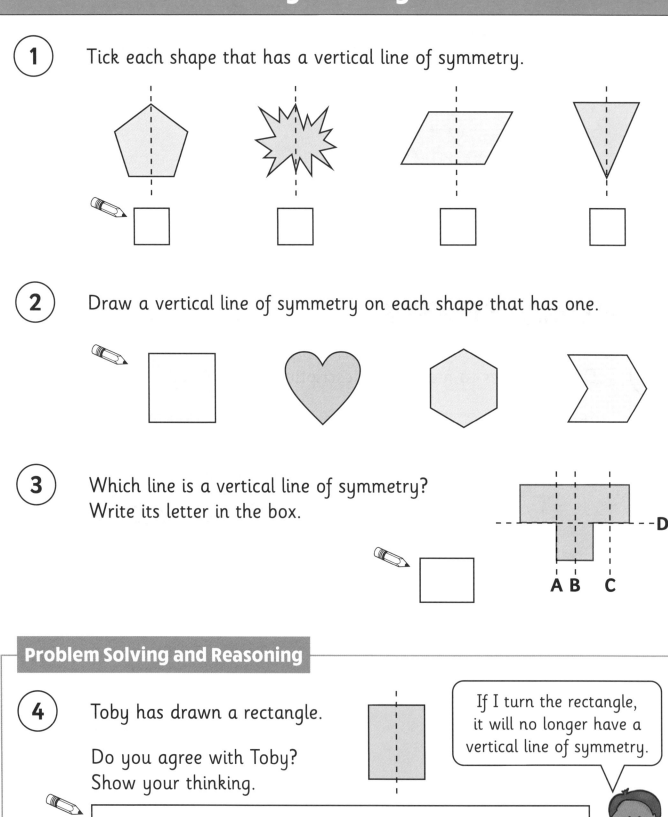

2 Draw a vertical line of symmetry on each shape that has one.

3 Which line is a vertical line of symmetry?
Write its letter in the box.

Problem Solving and Reasoning

4 Toby has drawn a rectangle.

Do you agree with Toby?
Show your thinking.

> If I turn the rectangle, it will no longer have a vertical line of symmetry.

Can you spot vertical lines of symmetry?

More Symmetry

1 Draw the missing half of each rectangle.

Each dashed line shows a vertical line of symmetry.

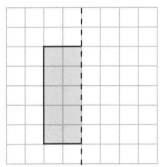 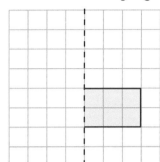 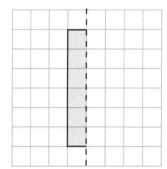

2 Draw the missing half of each shape.

Each dashed line shows a vertical line of symmetry.

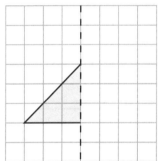 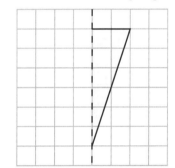 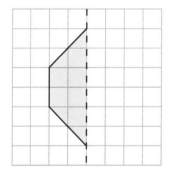

Problem Solving and Reasoning

3 Complete the drawings to make each one symmetrical.

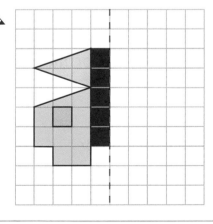 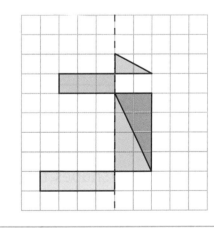 

Can you use lines of symmetry to draw shapes?

Sorting 2D Shapes

1 Draw two rings to sort these shapes by colour.

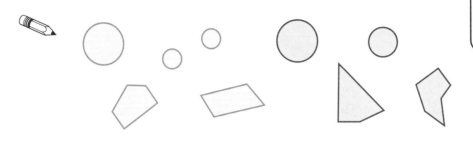

Are there different ways to sort these shapes?

2 How are these shapes sorted? Label each group.

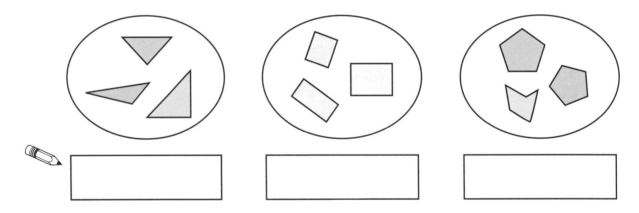

3 Draw lines to match each shape to the correct group.

| Fewer than 5 sides | 5 or more sides |

4 Serena has sorted these shapes in order of number of vertices. Circle the two shapes that need to swap places.

5 Give one way in which these shapes are sorted.

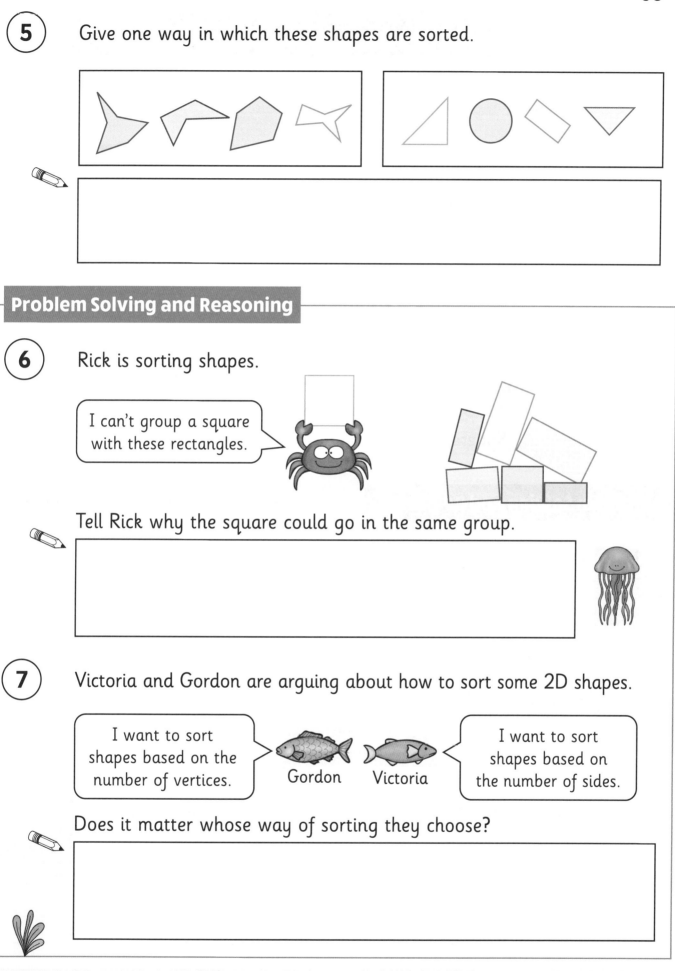

Problem Solving and Reasoning

6 Rick is sorting shapes.

I can't group a square with these rectangles.

Tell Rick why the square could go in the same group.

7 Victoria and Gordon are arguing about how to sort some 2D shapes.

I want to sort shapes based on the number of vertices.

Gordon   Victoria

I want to sort shapes based on the number of sides.

Does it matter whose way of sorting they choose?

Can you sort different 2D shapes?

Counting Faces of 3D Shapes

1 Write how many of each face the cuboid has.

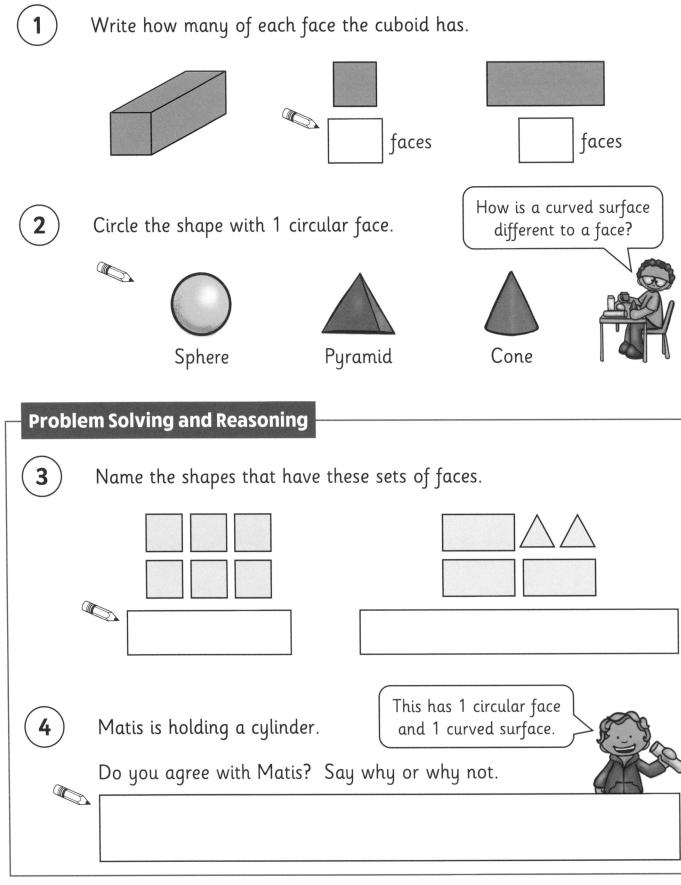

[ ] faces   [ ] faces

2 Circle the shape with 1 circular face.

How is a curved surface different to a face?

Sphere   Pyramid   Cone

Problem Solving and Reasoning

3 Name the shapes that have these sets of faces.

[ ]

[ ]

4 Matis is holding a cylinder.

This has 1 circular face and 1 curved surface.

Do you agree with Matis? Say why or why not.

[ ]

Do you know how many faces a 3D shape has?

Counting Edges of 3D Shapes

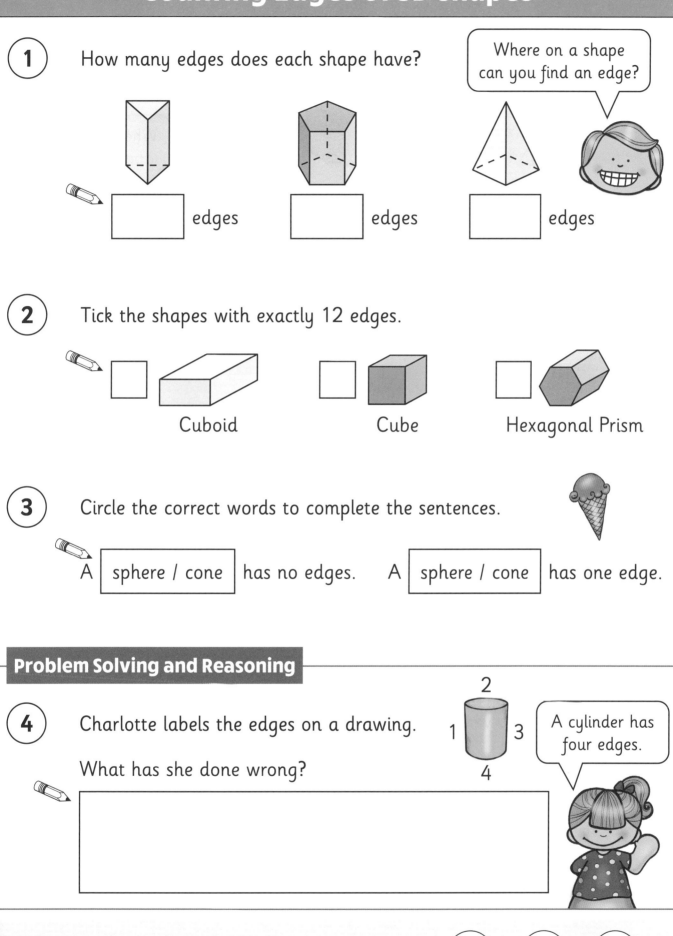

1 How many edges does each shape have?

Where on a shape can you find an edge?

☐ edges   ☐ edges   ☐ edges

2 Tick the shapes with exactly 12 edges.

☐ Cuboid   ☐ Cube   ☐ Hexagonal Prism

3 Circle the correct words to complete the sentences.

A | sphere / cone | has no edges.   A | sphere / cone | has one edge.

Problem Solving and Reasoning

4 Charlotte labels the edges on a drawing.

What has she done wrong?

A cylinder has four edges.

2
1   3
4

☐

Are you able to count the edges on 3D shapes?

Counting Vertices of 3D Shapes

1 Circle each shape that has vertices.

> What's the difference between an edge and a vertex?

2 Draw lines to match each shape to its number of vertices.

1
4
5
8

Problem Solving and Reasoning

3 The number of vertices on each prism follows a pattern.

Triangular prism
6 vertices

Cuboid
8 vertices

Pentagonal prism
10 vertices

How many vertices does a hexagonal prism have? Why?

Can you count the vertices on 3D shapes?

Sorting 3D Shapes

1 Circle the shape that doesn't fit in the group.

2 Draw two rings to sort these shapes into two groups.

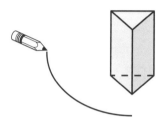

Odd number of faces   Even number of faces

3 Draw lines to match each shape to the correct group.

| Has a curved surface | No curved surfaces |

How else could you sort shapes?

4 How are these shapes sorted? Fill in the gaps to label the groups.

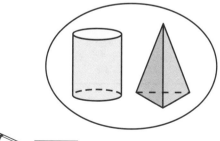 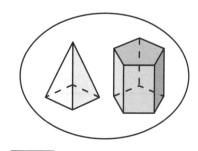

☐ or fewer vertices   ☐ or more vertices

5 Sort the shapes in order from fewest to most sides.

A Pentagonal prism **B** Sphere **C** Triangular prism **D** Hexagonal prism

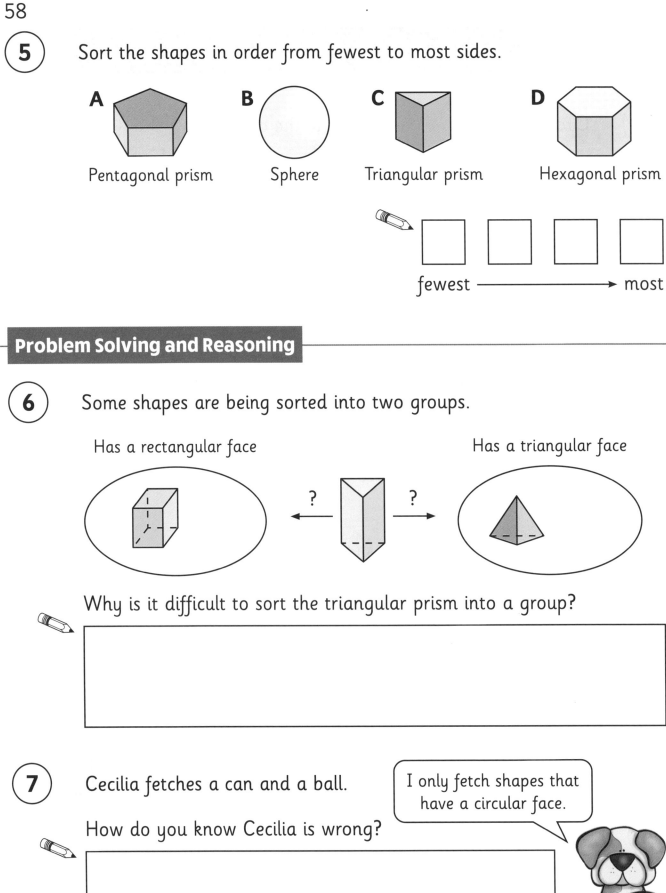

fewest ⟶ most

Problem Solving and Reasoning

6 Some shapes are being sorted into two groups.

Has a rectangular face   Has a triangular face

? ←   → ?

Why is it difficult to sort the triangular prism into a group?

7 Cecilia fetches a can and a ball.

How do you know Cecilia is wrong?

> I only fetch shapes that have a circular face.

Can you compare different 3D shapes?

Shape Patterns

1 Draw the next shape in each pattern.

2 Tick the shape that will come 9th in this pattern.

3 Two shapes are missing from this pattern.

▲ ☐ ? ? ☐ ⬠ ▲

Tick the shapes that fill the gap.

4 Draw two more shapes to make the pattern symmetrical.

5 Draw a ring around each pattern that is symmetrical.

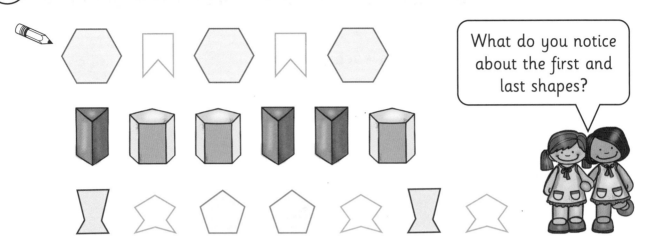

What do you notice about the first and last shapes?

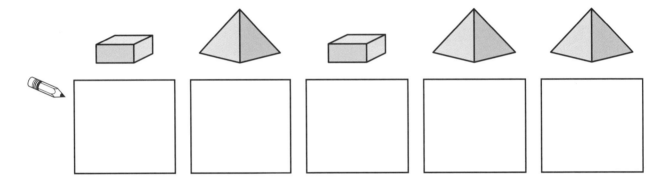

Problem Solving and Reasoning

6 Draw the shapes in a different order to make a symmetrical pattern.

7 Max sees a pattern of circles and stars.

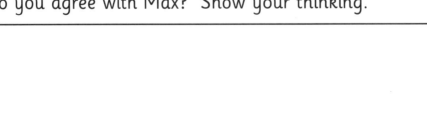

The 2nd shape is a star, so the 20th shape will also be a star.

Do you agree with Max? Show your thinking.

Can you see when different patterns are made?